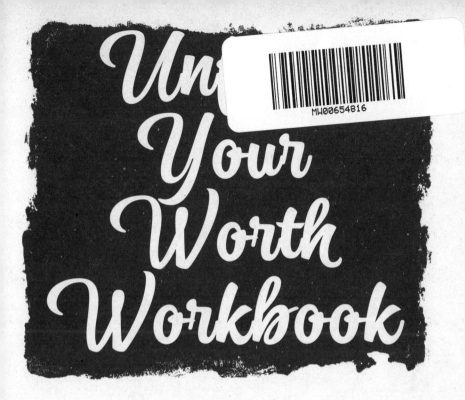

Un... Your Worth Workbook

Faith G. Harper,
PhD, LPC-S, ACS, ACN

Unfuck Your Worth Workbook

MANAGE YOUR MONEY, VALUE YOUR OWN LABOR, AND STOP FINANCIAL FREAKOUTS IN A CAPITALIST HELLSCAPE

Faith G. Harper,
PhD, LPC-S, ACS, ACN

Microcosm Publishing
Portland, OR

UNFUCK YOUR WORTH WORKBOOK

Manage Your Money, Value Your Own Labor, and Stop Financial Freakouts in a Capitalist Hellscape

Part of the 5 Minute Therapy Series

© Dr. Faith Harper, 2020

This edition © Microcosm Publishing, 2020

First edition, first published August 25, 2020

ISBN 9781621061786

This is Microcosm #551

Cover and design by Joe Biel

Edited by Elly Blue

For a catalog, write or visit:

Microcosm Publishing

2752 N Williams Ave.

Portland, OR 97227

503-799-2698

www.microcompublishing.com

These worksheets can be used on their own, or as a companion to **Unfuck Your Worth** by Dr. Faith G. Harper.

These worksheets are free to reproduce but no more than two can be reproduced in a publication without expressed permission from the publisher.

To join the ranks of high-class stores that feature Microcosm titles, talk to your rep: In the U.S. **Como** (Atlantic), **Fujii** (Midwest), **Book Travelers West** (Pacific), **Turnaround** in Europe, **Manda/UTP** in Canada, **New South** in Australia, and **GPS** in Asia, India, Africa, and South America. Sold in the gift market by **Gifts of Nature**

Did you know that you can buy our books directly from us at sliding scale rates? Support a small, independent publisher and pay less than Amazon's price at www.Microcosm.Pub

Global labor conditions are bad, and our roots in industrial Cleveland in the 70s and 80s made us appreciate the need to treat workers right. Therefore, our books are MADE IN THE USA.

MICROCOSM · PUBLISHING

Microcosm Publishing is Portland's most diversified publishing house and distributor with a focus on the colorful, authentic, and empowering. Our books and zines have put your power in your hands since 1996, equipping readers to make positive changes in their lives and in the world around them. Microcosm emphasizes skill-building, showing hidden histories, and fostering creativity through challenging conventional publishing wisdom with books and bookettes about DIY skills, food, bicycling, gender, self-care, and social justice. What was once a distro and record label was started by Joe Biel in his bedroom and has become among the oldest independent publishing houses in Portland, OR. We are a politically moderate, centrist publisher in a world that has inched to the right for the past 80 years.

TABLE OF CONTENTS

Unfuck Your Budget 47

Unfuck Your Spending on Must-Haves 77

INTRODUCTION

Hey there, workbook person!

This workbook is full of actionable ideas from my book Unfuck Your Worth, which is about the brain science and cultural constructs and emotional content around money. It's the "underneath" part of dealing with money and worth issues.

Money is emotional, scary, complicated, and gross. Our interactions with it generally feel shitty. All of the many lovely, pragmatic financial planning books we buy end up gathering dust because we don't feel pragmatic about money. Then, because we have assigned it a central focus in our lives, in this weird, theoretical, culturally-agreed-upon way, we get fucked up about it. The worth we assign to ourselves and others gets tied into our experiences with money.

Money can make us sad and scared. And shitty and mean. And frustrated and self-recriminating and avoidant. Nothing brings out our worst selves more than money does. Well, that and sex. But I already wrote that book.

Why does money fuck us up so badly? A lot of it has to do with trauma, both individual and societal. A lot of it has to do with capitalism. The way we are fucked up about money makes us equate our worth as people with our class or our income or the size of our house or car, or our savings or our clothes or our job or our ability to work. Money makes us forget our true worth, which has nothing to do with money.

Ultimately, the way to unfuck our worth is to understand that money is energy. Not in a magic, woo-woo kind of way but in material terms of time, labor, and communication. Thinking about money as energy that we expend, take in, exchange, or share, instead of as a barometer of our worth helps overcome the trauma. So does supporting each other as we do this hard, scary work.

This workbook is about our emotional relationship with money and how it's influenced by fucking trauma and other brain-wiring survival instincts. It's about how the value of a dollar becomes equated with the value of our personhood.

And about how all of those issues make it seem utterly out of reach to even think about creating a workable budget and getting ahead in ways that are meaningful to you.

Because if you are fucked up about money that means the system is working.

Conflating the value of your personhood with the money in your pocket? Operating from a place of trauma-influenced chaos? Carrying tons of debt? Paying tons of interest? Spending money in ways that advertisers tell you will make you feel better instead of in ways that actually make you feel better? Any or all of the above means the current economic system makes mad bank off of you. And then it tells you it's your fault that your shit isn't together. As long as we all believe that to be true, the capitalist hellscape mentioned in the title of the book stays alive. And I'm so over all of that, what about you?

Some of the exercises in this workbook are about the practical nuts and bolts of managing your money, it's super overwhelming. So I assigned myself the job of doing the research and sifting through all that noise, finding the most solid advice, and creating worksheets around that advice. We've got worksheets for you to track your spending, work out a budget, save towards your goals, pay down your debt, and more financial nitty gritty stuff.

BUUUUT, this isn't just a financial unfuckery workbook. Most of the exercises here are about unfucking not just your money but your baggage around money and how that is affecting your sense of self-worth. You know. Figuring out your values, wants, and needs, setting good boundaries, and recognizing what areas you need to work on so you can have your best life.

Since I write practical books that are designed to help you do important shit to heal yourself and your life it can be far more helpful for a lot of people to not just read about practical strategies but to work through them. Can you use this workbook without the book? Totally. All instructions for each worksheet are included. Will some of them make more sense if you read the book? Also totally. But I don't ever want anyone to feel that they got tricked into having to buy more than they intended to buy. The book and the workbook are designed to work alone, but wonder-twin activate and be even stronger together. No worries either way.

Financial Fear Mindfulness Practice

When you find yourself stuck and overwhelmed by financial fears, try feeling it without letting it take over. Our thoughts and feelings change the minute we start paying attention to them in a mindful way. It's like examining something under a microscope: the minute you turn on the light so you can see better, whatever you are looking at starts to react to the light.

1) **Experience the present.**

   What's going on right now? What are you thinking? Feeling? What's going on in your body?

2) **Take a deeper dive.**

   Where are these feelings in your body? How big or small? How strong or weak? The thoughts you are experiencing, how do they sound?

3) **Take off the judgy-pants.**

   Just notice all of these experiences (thoughts, feelings, somatic responses) as something you have. Not something you are. Make yourself a judgement-free zone. They are not good or bad, they are just information from your body in the present moment that are activated by your experiences of financial fear. Right now we aren't worried about fixing anything, just listening to ourselves.

4) **Practice self-compassion.**

   Think of someone who you love. A friend, a family member. Someone who is fundamentally a good person who has made mistakes but always gets back up and tries their hardest. What would you tell that person if they were going through this experience. Got an idea? Cool. Now tell *yourself* that.

COAL

When those financial fears get to be too much and you're overwhelmed, anxious, or upset, here's, a simple exercise that you can use when you're working through this book, and your regular life. Dan Siegal came up with the acronym COAL, which expands on the idea that shining a light on the hard stuff fundamentally changes our relationship with it...which is the biggest part of making positive changes in our lives.

COAL stands for:

Curiosity

Openness

Acceptance

Love

So as you read this book, if you find yourself getting anxious or upset, remember COAL and see if you can disrupt the cycle of feeling bad about feeling bad.

Noticing what you're upset about is important because that's probably where you can do the best work. When we start approaching our own minds with this level of respect, we recenter our worth. This is good shit. It takes practice. Like, a lot of practice. But it helps us keep our worth in its rightful place while we do all the heavy unfuckening work around money and all those other esteem-killers

Self-compassion

Part of unfucking your worth is to *stop beating yourself up*. Researchers have repeatedly demonstrated that self-flagellation doesn't help us make positive changes. Weirdly, telling yourself you are terrible doesn't make you change your habits...it just reinforces the idea that you don't deserve to live your best life.

Let's start challenging that negative frame. I want you to think of someone you love, maybe a friend who is flawed, who has had a tough history, but still working hard to make good changes in their life. I want you to picture how you would be compassionate and encouraging as they struggle with that journey and write them a little letter.

Cool. Got it? Now this is *yours*. This is your self-encouragement framed with compassion about how fucking difficult it is to make these changes. I want you to come back to this letter as often as you need to, and read it at least twice whenever you catch yourself beating yourself up.

UNFUCK YOUR RELATIONSHIP WITH MONEY

The first chapter of this workbook is all about figuring out what money *means to you*—and if you want to change that relationship going forward. We'll take a real look at our values and internalized messages about finances...and how our individual histories have shaped them. This is where we really learn about ourselves so we can make thoughtful changes going forward. (I know, gross. But if we don't do the emotional work first, the financial work won't stick, trust Auntie Faith.)

If you're doing this work with a partner (or anyone you share finances with), it's a good idea to fill out the worksheets in this chapter by yourself. Your experiences and values will be different and it's better to know those differences.

Word Association

Say the word "money" out loud. What words, phrases, memories, or images come to mind with that word? What feelings do you associate with those thoughts? Write them here. If these feelings are extra-intense, go through the COAL exercise, or your go-to activation-management coping skill.

Now ask these questions out loud (maybe not in the middle of the coffee shop, though, OK?) and then write down the words, phrases, memories, or images that come up:

What do you need to survive?

What do you need to be happy?

What are you working towards?

What does accomplishing that goal mean for you?

What is your ideal relationship with money?

Do you currently have a good sense of your available funds, debts, and spending?

How does your current understanding of your finances make you feel?

Are there any spending changes you'd like to make? Which ones?

Are there any changes in your earnings that you'd like to make? Which ones?

Are there any changes in your savings or debts that you'd like to make? Which ones?

What does "earning enough money" mean to you?

What does saving money mean to you?

What does debt mean to you?

What does financial security look like for you?

If Money Were a Person, Who Would Your Person Be?

Ok, let's be honest. Money may be abstract, but it's an abstract thing that has a hugely tangible effect on your life, right? You are interacting with money as much as you are with the human beings in your life (unless you are completely, awesomely off the grid). So let's give your money the persona it honestly has anyway. Think about these questions and write down your answers.

Do you and money get along well?

What is the nature of your relationship?

What do you think about money?

How do you feel about money?

How does money treat you?

Your Money History

Human beings learn through mimicry, right? I mean, we learned to talk by listening to other people talk and figuring out that those sounds conveyed messages and we could make the same sounds. So we shouldn't feel bad that the ways our family and friends interact with money has influenced how we interact with money. It's just how we learn. But not all interactions are healthy, either. If we can recognize our financial habits within the context of the environment we learned them in, it is much easier to recognize the ones that don't serve us so we can work on replacing them with ones that do.

WHEN YOU WERE GROWING UP

What interactions did you have around your allowance, if you had one?

What about interactions around other money you were given (birthday money, babysitting money, etc.)?

What discussions about money do you remember?

Fights about money?

What financial topics were not talked about?

What things do you remember wanting that cost money? Did you get them?

What other things were purchased for you? Who made those decisions? What influenced those decisions?

What is your most positive childhood memory about money or how money was used (to buy something, do something, etc?)

What is your most negative childhood memory about money?

Anything that you noticed in these answers that surprised you? Or that you think might be an important influence on your relationship with money now?

Ok, ow. As much fun as that was, now we are gonna do it again with your life now. Think about your current family. Whether you are still embedded with your biological family or have one of your own. Think about your partners, past and present. Your closest friends. Your coworkers. The people you interact with on the regular.

IN YOUR LIFE NOW

What are your interactions about your income?

What about your interactions around other money you have or get (from family, partners, etc.)?

What discussions about money do you have?

What fights?

What money-related things are not talked about?

What things did you want in the recent past or want now that cost money? Did you or will you get them?

What kinds of things are purchased for you? Who made those decisions? What influenced those decisions?

What is your most positive adult memory about money or how money was used (to buy something, do something, etc.)?

What is your most negative adult memory about money?

Anything that you noticed in these answers that surprised you? Or that you realize has more influence on your life than you thought?

Internalized Messaging Check-in

Let's take a minute to see how money specifically is influencing your self-worth, okay?

Complete the following sentences with your own answers:

Poor people are . . .

Rich people are . . .

I am . . .

We all create internal "rules" about how the world works based on what we experience. What rules about worth did you notice in yourself when answering these questions?

Your Experiences around Systemic Wealth Inequality

Systemic wealth inequality refers to the mechanisms in which society has been designed to maintain a status quo of the have and have-nots. Poverty is insidious and pervasive and intentionally maintained in order to control those of us who don't have power by those who do.

Some questions to explore and discuss:

How was systemic wealth inequality and underpaid labor viewed as you were growing up? Were these issues you were made aware of? Educated about? How so?

How is systemic wealth inequality and underpaid labor viewed and discussed within your current household? Friends and peers? How so?

Have you noticed any tendencies in yourself to treat underpaid labor differently from appropriately compensated labor? How so? Any particular circumstances that make it more likely?

What is one immediate thing you can do that demonstrates a respect for the value of underpaid labor within your social circle?

How can you create ongoing support for individuals providing underpaid labor within your social circle?

How do you feel about the decriminalization of sex work industries? What concerns do you have? How have you seen sex work portrayed in media? How was it discussed when you were growing up? How is it discussed among your peer group?

Your Experiences around Unpaid Labor

We have been socially encouraged to value unpaid labor differently from paid labor. Unpaid labor refers to the work we all do that we do not receive direct payment for, such as child rearing or completing household chores. Some of us do more unpaid labor than others. And we have all been subjected to messages about the value of these different forms of labor.

How were paid and unpaid labor viewed as you were growing up? Were they centered and respected differently? How so?

How is paid and unpaid labor viewed and discussed within your current household? Friends and peers? Are they centered and respected differently? How so?

Have you noticed any tendencies in yourself to treat unpaid labor differently from paid labor? Howso? Any particular circumstances that make it more likely?

What is one immediate thing you can do that demonstrates a respect for the value of unpaid labor within your social circle?

How can you create ongoing support for unpaid labor within your social circle?

Your Experiences with Affluenza

I don't think it's a huge surprise to anyone, that poverty is related to poor mental health outcomes. But, as I mentioned in Unfuck Your Worth, wealth, ideas about wealth, and strivings for wealth can also be very toxic. "Affluenza" is a fairly recent term coined to describe the unhealthy psychological and social effects that affluence can have on individuals. It can create feelings of guilt, social isolation, and a lack of motivation for personal growth and achievement. You don't have to be a 1%er to have internalized a whole lot of ideas about class essentialism and the superiority of wealth and these messages can really take a toll on your self-worth.

What messages have you received about money equalling worth and value in society? Where did these messages come from?

Have you ever felt less-than because you had a lower salary, less money in the bank, or couldn't afford to own expensive items?

Have you ever felt a sense of superiority over others because of what you had or could afford to have?

Have you ever used the money you had to prop up your ego or self-esteem?

Have you ever made decisions that were based on the pursuit of money for its own sake?

How are finances discussed in your family/social circle? Are purchases bragged about? Payoffs discussed as a cost of making life easier?

What brings value and meaning to your life that is not directly influenced by money?

FINANCIAL TRAUMA

A short definition of trauma: It's a response created by your amygdala to try to protect you from re-experiencing difficult events. The amygdala is part of the limbic system, which is the part of the brain that connects and stories memories and emotions. Not the how-to-get-to-the-grocery-store memories, but the big life events memories. The amygdala's job is to keep you alive by assigning labels to certain events that have happened to you so it can help you stay safe in the future by remembering if a Big Life Event ended well or not.

If something happens that reminds you of a traumatic event, your amygdala hijacks your response system in an effort to protect you from being re-traumatized. So some location, or smell, or sensation, or something sends you right back to the traumatic event. When this happens you might start responding to your present life as if you are still in your past life, and still in your trauma experience of the previous Big Life Event—responding to your current surroundings as if you are literally being retraumatized.

This is not a bad thing in and of itself. If you trip on broken concrete and fall on your ass, that's the kind of thing you want to remember and watch out for in the future at an unconscious, automatic level. Especially if you walk down that sidewalk every day and the city isn't going to fix the problem anytime soon.

But the amygdala doesn't discriminate—it's going to err on the side of caution. So we get a danger cue from all kinds of random pieces of the environment that don't actually pose a threat. Like if all sidewalk cracks get you turnt and you freeze in panic. When this happens again and again and you can't get out of it, that's a trauma response. Which oftentimes leads to post-traumatic stress disorder (PTSD).

While studying financial personalities, research psychologist Galen Buckwalter kept bumping into something weird. He was working with a "factor model" (a way to classify groups of personality traits) called HEXACO, which stands for honesty/humility, emotionality, extroversion, agreeableness, conscientiousness, openness. His hypothesis was that everyone would show some combination of these traits, either positively or negatively, in their attitudes about money. But in researching actual humans, Dr. Buckwalter kept finding traits that didn't fall into any of those categories. But these traits did align with how humans experience fear.

When unpacking the life circumstances of the individuals participating in his research, he found that those who presented with fear around money issues were experiencing the same kinds of symptoms he had seen when studying trauma and PTSD earlier in his career.

Yes, I know that "financial PTSD" doesn't actually exist as a diagnosis. And financial issues alone don't qualify anyone for a general PTSD diagnosis. But hang with me. Let's look at how PTSD is diagnosed:

- Intrusive thoughts (flashbacks, involuntary memories, stuck in anxious thinking patterns, upsetting dreams and nightmares).

- Avoiding reminders of the traumatic event (situations, people, places, activities, objects) and resisting talking about what happened and their feelings surrounding the event.

- Negative and often distorted thoughts and feelings about oneself or other people and/or feeling detached from others or from activities that used to be enjoyable.

- Arousal and reactive symptoms like irritability and anger, reckless or self-destructive behavior, struggles with sleeping or concentration. These symptoms are indicative of our body's allostatic load, which is defined by the International Encyclopedia of the Social & Behavioral Sciences, as "the cost of chronic exposure to elevated or fluctuating endocrine or neural responses resulting from chronic or repeated challenges that the individual experiences as stressful" which is just a fancy way of saying the body gets overwhelmed by trauma as much as the brain does.

Dr. Buckwalter went on to define financial PTSD as *"the physical, emotional, and cognitive deficits people experience when they cannot cope with either abrupt financial loss or the chronic stress of having inadequate financial resources."*

He has found that 23% of all adults (and 36% of millennials because society has fucked y'all over extra much) show symptoms of financial PTSD. And it only takes one of two things to happen. Either a big traumatic financial loss (losing a job, foreclosing a home, a shitty divorce settlement) or 3+ months of not having enough income to meet one's monthly expenses.

Now let's look at what Dr. Buckwalter found in the people who were demonstrating financial PTSD:

- Rumination on financial failure

- Negative thought processes about money in general

- Perseveration about financial doom

- Seeing the world as fundamentally hostile and that it's only a matter of time before shit's fucked again

- Avoidance of the mail, phone calls, etc. (because, bill collectors)

- Allostatic load is over the top. People are jittery, not sleeping well, have nightmares

- Little experience of joy and meaning

- Increase in unhealthy coping mechanisms like substance use or other avoidance strategies

- Isolation from others (especially if their financial PTSD was related to coercive control)

Sound familiar? Let's get to work

Financial Trauma Symptoms

What symptoms have you experienced due to poverty, financial stress, or financial overwhelmnment within the following categories? If you've got a lot to say, especially about current symptoms, its important to honor that you are working through trauma (and, fwiw, this is exactly what therapy is for).

Intrusive thoughts (e.g. flashbacks, involuntary memories, stuck in anxious thinking patterns, upsetting dreams and nightmares).

In the past:

Currently:

Avoiding reminders of the traumatic event (situations, people, places, activities, objects) and resisting talking about what happened and your feelings surrounding the event.

In the past:

Currently:

Negative and often distorted thoughts and feelings (ongoing, distorted beliefs about oneself or others and/or feeling detached from others or from activities that used to be enjoyable).

In the past:

Currently:

Arousal and reactive symptoms (irritability and anger, reckless or self-destructive behavior, struggles with sleeping or concentration).

In the past:

Currently:

Test Your Financial Thinking

Trauma reactions often lead to us framing everything in a negative light. We start to expect that everything will be fucked all of the time. Cognitive Behavioral Therapy is super helpful in framing how to unpack and challenge that constant negativity. This is a classic CBT skill framed specifically for financial PTSD.

What's the financial situation that you are focused on right now?

What are you thinking or imagining is happening or going to happen?

What emotions are you experiencing?

What bodily sensations?

What makes me think that my thoughts are true? Any evidence?

What makes me think my thoughts are not true (or not completely true)? Any evidence?

What's another way you can look at this situation that's more helpful?

What's the worst thing that can happen?

What could you do then?

What's the ideal outcome?

What would you do then?

What's the most probable outcome?

What can you do then?

What might be different if I change my thinking?

If I was giving advice to a friend going through this same thing, what would I tell them?

UNFUCK YOUR VALUES

Values is another one of those terms that we seen thrown around in a way that makes us think, "Wow, super important" and almost simultaneously "What the fuck does that mean, though?" What's interesting about the word "value" is that it is a synonym of the word worth. It means *what we hold in high regard*. What deserves our attention.

What is most important to you in life? How we describe ourselves and perceive ourselves is usually a reflection of our values. Our decisions and boundaries about our money and labor should come from what we hold most valuable.

If there is a disconnect between our values and our actions, this is a chance to pay attention to that experience and set ourselves back on course.

The big challenge with many people is defining what our values are, rather than the values that others have imposed upon us—whether parents or other caretakers when we were young, our friends, peers, and partners, or society as a whole.

We'll get to money-specific values in the Budget chapter of this workbook, and in the Work chapter, we'll . For now your goal is to figure out your bigger-picture values that drive all your life decisions, including money.

Values Identification

Many people don't have a language to articulate their values. So here's a huge list of potential values, plus space to write in more of your own. Circle the ones that are important to you. Then use a different color pen or pencil to circle ones that aren't currently prominent in your life but that you *want* to be more important to you.

Badassitude

Accountability

Accuracy

Achievement

Adaptability

Advocacy

Allyship

Ambition

Artistic expression

Artistic interactions

Assertive

Attentive

Balance

Beauty

Boldness

Bravery

Brilliance

Calm

Candor

Carefulness

Certainty

Challenge

Clean

Clear

Clever

Comfort

Commitment

Common sense

Communication

Community

Compassion for animals

Compassion for fellow humans

Competence

Concentration

Confidence

Connection

Consciousness

Consistency

Contentment

Contribution

Control

Convenience

Conviction

Cool

Cooperation

Courage

Courtesy

Creation

Creativity

Credibility

Curiosity

Decisiveness

Defeating fascism

Dependability

Design

Determination

Development

Devotion

Dignity

Discipline

Discovery

Dismantling oppressive systems

Dynamic'

Effective

Efficient

Empathy

Empowerment

Endurance

Energy

Enjoyment

Enthusiasm

Social Justice

Ethical

Excellence

Experience

Exploration

Expressive

Fairness

Family

Fame

Fearless

Feelings

Feminism

Intersectionality

Ferocious

Fidelity

Focus

Foresight

Fortitude	Inspiring	Patience
Freedom	Integrity	Peace
Friendship	Intelligence	Performance
Fun	Intensity	Persistence
Generosity	Intuition	Physicality
Genius	Irreverent	Playfulness
Giving	Joy	Poise
Goodness	Justice	Potential
Grace	Kindness	Power
Gratitude	Knowledge	Practical
Greatness	Lawful	Present
Growth	Leadership	Productivity
Happiness	Learning	Professionalism
Hard work	Logic	Prosperity
Tenacity	Love	Purpose
Hard-working	Loyalty	Queerness
Harmony	Magic	Questioning authority
Health	Mastery	Realistic
Honesty	Maturity	Reason
Honor	Meaning	Recognition
Hope	Moderation	Reflective
Humility	Motivation	Relaxation
Humor	Nazi-Punching	Representation
Hygge	Nesting	Respect
Imagination	Neutrality	Responsibility
Independence	Openness	Results-oriented
Individuality	Optimism	Righteousness
Influence	Organization	Rigor
Innovation	Originality	Risk
Insight	Passion	Satisfaction

Security
Self-care
Self-compassion
Self-reliance
Selflessness
Sensitivity
Serenity
Service
Sexuality
Sharing
Silence
Simplicity
Sincerity
Skill
Solitude
Spiritual
Spontaneous
Stability
Status
Stewardship
Storytelling
Strength
Structure
Success
Support
Surprise
Tree-hugging
Teamwork
Sobriety
Thorough

Thoughtful
Timeliness
Tolerance
Toughness
Traditional
Transparency
Trust
Truth
Understanding
Uniqueness
Unity
Vigor
Vision
Vulnerability
Wealth
Welcoming
Winning
Wisdom
Wonder

Have values that aren't on this list?
Write in your own.

Map Your Values

VALUES FROM THE PEOPLE WHO RAISED ME (PARENTS, GUARDIANS, OTHER FAMILY MEMBERS, ETC.)

VALUES FROM OTHER IMPORTANT PEOPLE IN MY LIFE (FRIENDS, PARTNERS)

VALUES SPECIFIC TO MY LOCAL COMMUNITY/CULTURAL HERITAGE

VALUES FROM MY LARGER COMMUNITY

VALUES I WOULD MOST LIKE TO LIVE BY

VALUES I AM CURRENTLY LIVING BY

My Authentic Self

Here's a place to take the core elements of the work you did regarding your personal values to create a snapshot of your essential identity.

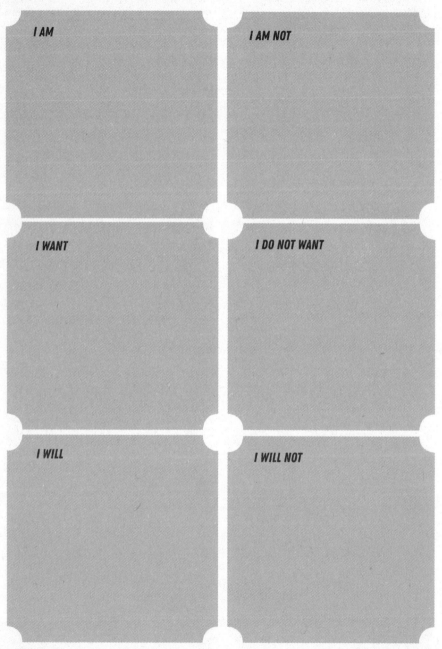

I AM

I AM NOT

I WANT

I DO NOT WANT

I WILL

I WILL NOT

Honoring Your Values

Now let's put those values to work. You've got your core values listed (good work, there!) and you used it to distill down some fundamentals about your authentic self (kicking workbook ass!!!!). Now, here is the place to funnel those ideas into action.

Use this worksheet to plan out how you'll achieve or experience the values you identified as the ones you would most like to live by. You can focus on changes you want to make around how you earn, spend, save, or feel about money, or anything else that's becoming clear to you while doing these exercises.

VALUE	ACTIONS I NEED TO TAKE	LIMITS I NEED TO SET

Your Best Possible Future Self

This exercise was developed by Laura King and has been found to be incredibly effective in multiple controlled studies.

Stop reading this. Close your eyes. Spend a few minutes imagining your best possible self ten years from now. Don't worry about the details of getting there. Just what your best possible future will be like. You can write it down if you want, but you don't have to. You can visualize it, or tell yourself the story, draw a picture, or ...

Research shows that if you spend 20 minutes a day for four days on this exercise it does amazing things for your optimism about life. So do the thing. Four days in a row.

UNFUCK YOUR BUDGET

Now we get to the numbers! Budgeting is the difficult work of looking at your short term values and long term strategies to living the life you want for yourself.

In the non-workbook version of *Unfuck Your Worth*, I talk about budgeting as a radical form of self-care. Self-care care is far more than face masks and bubble baths (though, okay, I love those too). It can include dealing with our trauma histories. Getting our teeth cleaned. Spending all day on the phone setting up a student loan payment plan. Dealing with the capitalist hellscape with eyes wide open and full awareness. And budgeting. Which is where we're going to start.

Budgeting can be one of the scariest things we do financially. Why? Oftentimes not knowing the full extent of something feels safer. The scientific term for that is *experiential avoidance*. If we perceive something as a threat, we will try to inhibit our emotions and suppress our thoughts around that experience. It's good old-fashioned post-trauma brain wiring again.

So we are going to sneak around our experiential avoidance by starting with the positives. Our values. After we have them up on the forefront of our minds, we are going to move on to the nuts and bolts of getting our budget in line with those values.

Your Money Values

All of the decisions you make about money should be grounded within your value system, not the value system others have foisted upon you. Figuring out what is what helps you determine if you are operating in a healthy money space and if you have enough money to live your values.

This is different from the big-picture values exercises earlier in the book, which was about what you want to focus on in your life. Your money values, by contrast, are the financial resources you put behind that focus. For example if you value independence you might find yourself choosing different money values than if creativity tops your list.

So let's start with the following list of things that may or may not have value to you, that are cost-associated (that is, shit we generally have to spend money on to access).

- Transportation (car and related car expenses, bike and biking gear, cab or rideshare fares, bus passes)
- Housing (new place, dream home, vacation home, etc.)
- Renovations/Upgrades/Household Projects
- Art or art supplies
- MORE BOOOOOOOOOOKS
- Music
- Computer (or other tech) hardware or software
- Games, gaming equipment, tournament entry
- Creative endeavours (art supplies, instruments, recording equipment, etc. either as a business or for the sake of creation)
- Business investments
- Joining and otherwise supporting an organization
- Emergency funds
- Retirement savings/Long-term investments
- Sports/Hobbies/Athletics
- Eating out/Social activities

- Paying someone to manage tasks for you (domestic labor, personal assistant, etc.)

- Clothing/Accessories/Grooming/Personal appearance

- Charitable giving (either directly to people in need or through an organization)

- Vacation/Travel

- School/Education/Continued learning (for yourself or a loved one)

- Medical treatments/Surgeries (stuff not covered by insurance)

- Paying down debt

- Paying back someone who had your back in the past

- Spending money on others (buying gifts, taking people out to eat, paying for a cousin's econ textbook, etc.)

- Other self-care that isn't covered by insurance (acupuncture, massage, coaching, healthier foods, sexual aids, etc.)

- Tipping well because people are out there working damn hard

Ok, now let's organize them. Add in whatever categories I left out that matter to you.

CONSISTENT PRIORITY	SOMETIMES IMPORTANT	EVERY ONCE IN A WHILE	ZERO IMPORTANCE TO ME

Prioritizing Within Your Money Values

Now that you have a sense of what you most value using money for, the next part of budget creation is finding ways to make that happen. If we are looking to do things that are important to our core, authentic selves, that fundamentally shifts how we approach the problem. If our goal is to put money into monthly massages, giving up the monthly sushi in pursuit of our goal doesn't activate our internal obstinance. And having to hunker down on some side-hustles doesn't feel like spitting on a forest fire, because you have a plan in place where you can really see the results of your extra work.

The point of this exercise is to blow out the cobwebs of OPP (which, in this case, means Other People's *Priorities*) and re-center in what *your* authentic financial priorities are. If we are going to look at spending habits, reality-based budgets, dream budgets, and the like, they should be centered on what has meaning and joy for *you*.

Now that you have your priorities laid out clearly in front of you, answer these questions:

If you had an extra $100 dollars right now, where would it go?

What category or categories does that expenditure fall under? Break it down. For instance a massage might include the categories "self-care," "transportation," and "tipping well."

Did the categories align with ones you consider higher priority?

If not, was it because of the unique circumstances you are currently experiencing?

How were your priorities different than what you originally thought?

Now what if it's $1000?

What about $10,000?

Make a Dream Expenditures List

Now you've done all this work unpacking the stuff that is most important for you to spend money on, good for you The next two exercises aren't about what is possible in the present, but paying attention to what's important as you move into the future.

List out your big-ticket wish list items. Things that aren't recurring monthly expenses but require a hefty payout upfront. You define hefty: That could mean $100 or $100k. Your list might include things like a big trip, training or school, refinishing your bathtub, fixing your grandma's antique watch, buying a home, or whatever else you would like to do if money wasn't a consideration. Put a star or number next to your highest priorities:

Now list out the regular monthly expenditures you'd have room for in a dream budget. Things like weekly massages, bi-weekly therapy, a luxe organic grocery budget, dinners out with friends, paying down student loans from hell, etc.). Put a star or number by your highest priorities:

PRIORITY	DREAM EXPENDITURES

Tina's Money Spell

About 20 years ago, my friend Tina suggested we do this journaling activity together. Tina is Wiccan, so we called it the money spell. Not because we were burning dragon's blood resin in the woods, but because we were looking at how we energetically get in our own way in terms of money. We found we had been focusing on our distressing short-term money shortfalls without ever looking at our longer-term goals.

Doing this activity was my starting point for applying for grad school to become a therapist and Tina starting his life coaching certification. Because as we pushed ourselves past short-term thinking (my car payment is 60 days overdue, I have to hide the car from being repossessed) to longer-term goals, we had to think differently about how we were going to get there and how that aligned with work we are passionate about.

Here is the idea: Imagine that you have an extra $1000 on the first day of the month and that doubles the second day ($2000). Your imaginary windfall continues to double each day after ($2000 becomes $4000 becomes $8000, etc). Write out how you would use that money every day for a month. You'll notice that we didn't do the math for you. Doing the math is part of the process of thinking about the bigger picture.

Some people find this activity really difficult. Financial trauma makes it incredibly difficult to plan for anything outside of our immediate panic. If you find you're having a lot of trouble, go back to the exercises way back in the introduction of this book to help.

DAY	BUDGET	WHAT YOU WILL DO WITH THE MONEY
Day 1	$1000	
Day 2		
Day 3		
Day 4		
Day 5		
Day 6		
Day 7		
Day 8		
Day 9		
Day 10		
Day 11		
Day 12		
Day 13		
Day 14		
Day 15		
Day 16		
Day 17		
Day 18		
Day 19		
Day 20		
Day 21		
Day 22		
Day 23		
Day 24		
Day 25		
Day 26		
Day 27		
Day 28		
Day 29		
Day 30		

Track Your Current Expenditures

Now make a nice mug of tea, take some deep breaths, and head into this one. No self-shaming, just information, okay? Use the interventions from earlier in the book, like COAL, to help manage any trauma activation, just like you would with any other trauma responses.

First, if you have bank statements (whether on paper or you can log in and look at them), look back over what you've spent in the past 90 days. Detail what money came in and what money went out. Maybe it's because I'm old, but I think this is easiest to do on paper with a color code for expenditures so you can see patterns at a glance (like green for bills, pink for food, etc). You don't have to add it all up unless you want to; the goal is to get a sense of where your money goes and give yourself a basis for comparison to your spending habits once you start paying closer attention. Though if you notice a big disconnect between how you are spending when you are paying attention to it, and when you aren't? You may want to go ahead and add it up to get a clearer sense of your patterns!

Now use the worksheets on the next pages to track your spending for a week. This is a good tool in becoming more mindful about where your money goes on the regular. What patterns are you noticing? Anything surprising to you? Anything out of alignment with your financial values? What is different from when you looked at your past, probably less mindful, spending habits, versus now when you are cognizant that you are tracking everything going out?

I'm including two expense trackers here—the first, daily, one is for people with a lot of expenses every day, so you can list them all out with plenty of room. Feel free to make copies (or use a notebook) to record multiple days. The second one fits a whole week onto one page, which may work better for some of you. I'm including five weeks worth of the latter so you can track a whole month's spending.

DAILY EXPENSE TRACKER

DATE	EXPENSE	AMOUNT	CASH/CHECK/ DEBIT/CREDIT

WEEKLY EXPENSE TRACKER: WEEK ONE

	EXPENSE	AMOUNT	PAYMENT TYPE
Monday			
Tuesday			
Wednesday			
Thursday			
Friday			
Saturday			
Sunday			

WEEKLY EXPENSE TRACKER: WEEK TWO

	EXPENSE	AMOUNT	PAYMENT TYPE
Monday			
Tuesday			
Wednesday			
Thursday			
Friday			
Saturday			
Sunday			

WEEKLY EXPENSE TRACKER: WEEK THREE

	EXPENSE	AMOUNT	PAYMENT TYPE
Monday			
Tuesday			
Wednesday			
Thursday			
Friday			
Saturday			
Sunday			

WEEKLY EXPENSE TRACKER: WEEK FOUR

	EXPENSE	AMOUNT	PAYMENT TYPE
Monday			
Tuesday			
Wednesday			
Thursday			
Friday			
Saturday			
Sunday			

WEEKLY EXPENSE TRACKER: WEEK FIVE

	EXPENSE	AMOUNT	PAYMENT TYPE
Monday			
Tuesday			
Wednesday			
Thursday			
Friday			
Saturday			
Sunday			

FOCUSED EXPENSE TRACKER

After that first month, consider continuing to track your spending. It's helpful to know where your money is really going, and can help hold you accountable to your goals. You can keep tracking all your spending forever—no kinkshaming if that's your thing. Or you can hone in on one particular type of spending that you want to work on. Maybe you want to spend less on alcohol or more on books, so it makes sense to keep a closer eye on those things. Or maybe you want to track your credit card spending or online shopping generally.

FOCUSED EXPENSE TRACKER WEEK ONE

What I'm Tracking: _____

	EXPENSE	AMOUNT	PAYMENT TYPE
Monday			
Tuesday			
Wednesday			
Thursday			
Friday			
Saturday			
Sunday			

FOCUSED EXPENSE TRACKER WEEK TWO

What I'm Tracking: _____

	EXPENSE	AMOUNT	PAYMENT TYPE
Monday			
Tuesday			
Wednesday			
Thursday			
Friday			
Saturday			
Sunday			

FOCUSED EXPENSE TRACKER WEEK THREE

What I'm Tracking:_____

	EXPENSE	AMOUNT	PAYMENT TYPE
Monday			
Tuesday			
Wednesday			
Thursday			
Friday			
Saturday			
Sunday			

FOCUSED EXPENSE TRACKER WEEK FOUR

What I'm Tracking: _____

	EXPENSE	*AMOUNT*	*PAYMENT TYPE*
Monday			
Tuesday			
Wednesday			
Thursday			
Friday			
Saturday			
Sunday			

FOCUSED EXPENSE TRACKER WEEK FIVE

What I'm Tracking: _____

	EXPENSE	AMOUNT	PAYMENT TYPE
Monday			
Tuesday			
Wednesday			
Thursday			
Friday			
Saturday			
Sunday			

Draft Your Starter Budget

Now that you have a month's worth of spending data, let's organize it. This is just a "where you are right now" budget. It's not your ideal, it's your reality.

Feel free to adjust the categories to work for you, and to separate out anything you know is deductible for your small business, or that is related to a value you want to do more or less of.

You might also need to research annual expenses that didn't come up in the month you spent tracking your spending. Things like taxes, insurance premiums, or annual donations. Or maybe you have income or spending that isn't the same every month. To fit irregular income or expenses into your monthly budget, divide the amount that you made or spent in the last year by 12 and use that number.

For simplicity's sake, let's just track income you actually have—so when you calculate your paycheck amount, subtract taxes or insurance that your employer withholds, check cashing fees, or any other money that might be yours on paper but that you never actually get. Likewise, don't include those things as expenses if you've already subtracted them from your income.

First, use these pages to write down all the income and expenses you can think of. Go through your spending logs, look up your bank and credit card statements, go through your bills, try to get down really good estimates for everything.

Income

Paychecks:

Other regular income (child support, rent from roommates, side hustle income, gifts, etc):

Total income:

Monthly Expenses

Rent/Mortgage:

Renter's or homeowners insurance (if separate):

Utilities (electricity, gas, water, sewer, trash):

Internet, cable, phones, streaming subscriptions:

Other housing expenses (property taxes, lawn care, housekeeping, HOA fees):

Basic groceries and household supplies:

Special groceries for holidays, celebratory dinners, etc:

Meals out:

Alcohol and other fun substances:

Snacks, treats, and other food/drink expenses:

Books, music, gaming stuff, tech stuff:

Public transportation:

Taxis/Rideshares:

Gas:

Parking/tolls:

Vehicle maintenance (Oil changes, inspections, bicycle repair, etc):

Vehicle insurance:

Vehicle loan:

Other transportation expenses:

Health insurance premiums (if not already accounted for in paycheck):

Payments on balances of past medical expenses:

Medication copays:

Appointment copays:

Other medical care paid out-of-pocket (e.g., acupuncture, neurofeedback, therapy, vision correction, dentist):

Child care/babysitting:

Child support (if not already accounted for in paycheck):

Money given/sent to other family members:

Clothing/shoes/jewelry:

Other personal care expenses (haircuts, pedis, etc):

Laundry (if not covered under other household expenses):

Activities (movies, museums, glo golf):

"Unnecessary" household items (candles, holiday decorations, floofy blankets)

Donations:

Subscriptions (magazines, patreons, newsletters, etc):

Membership expenses (clubs, gym, etc):

Fees for cashier's checks or money orders:

Prepaid cards like phone cards:

Bank or credit card fees:

Other capitalism-based "service" fees:

School costs (school supplies, tuition, student loan payments, gym uniforms, class pictures, that fucking popcorn the PTA sells):

Pet related expenses:

Credit card payments (current minimums):

Investment contributions:

Savings contributions:

Emergency fund contributions:

Other expenditures and fuckery not otherwise specified:

Total monthly expenses:

Budget Breakdown

Now break out the numbers you wrote in your budget above into three categories: Must-haves, Savings/debt, and Fun Stuff. Must-haves are the mandatory things that keep you alive and safe—rent, mortgage, utilities, groceries, healthcare, and minimum payments on unsecured debt. Debt and savings are self-explanatory. And the fun stuff is everything else, the stuff you can technically survive without but that expresses your values and makes life worth living.

MUST-HAVES	FUN STUFF	SAVINGS/DEBT

Now tally it up:

Must-haves:

Savings/debt:

Fun stuff:

Income:

Needs to Income ratio (get this by dividing your income by the "needs" category):

According to Elizabeth Warren, who came up with this metric in the book she co-wrote with her daughter, *All Your Worth*, your ideal balance is to have your must-haves at 50% of your income, your savings (and debt) at 20%, and fun stuff at 30%.

What are your percentages in real life?

Where do you want them to be?

Annual Budget

Want to keep up your budgeting mastery? Did the He-Man theme song just play in your head when you read that? If so, awesome! But either way, you can now use your numbers for the past month to set an annual budget. Budget in what you spent in an average month in the last year, unless you foresee changes or want to set a new goal to better fit your budget to your vision. Then fill in your actual spending every month for the next 12 months and use that data to make your budget for the next year even better.

If you like spreadsheets, you can get fancy with this and set one up to do the math for you, or use the sample one I have online at *http://microcosm.pub/worthsheets*. You can also add columns for past years' spending, to compare your changes and progress over time.

It may be helpful for you to use this budget as a tool to try to curb your spending in some areas, and give more focus to other things you spend on or save for. But remember, this budget is just a plan—and you can change your plan when your circumstances and priorities change. It's a tool, not a straightjacket.

EXPENSES	TOTAL BUDGET	MONTHLY BUDGET	JANUARY	FEBRUARY	MARCH	APRIL
Rent/Mortage						
Utilities						
Phone						
Groceries						
Transportation						
Entertainment						
Clothes						
Total Expenses						
Total Income						

AY	JUNE	JULY	AUGUST	SEPTEMBER	OCTOBER	NOVEMBER	DECEMBER

UNFUCK YOUR SPENDING ON MUST-HAVES

Now you have a sense of what your dream budget is, what your real budget is, and where those two budgets are very, very different. That's okay, though. Hiding from reality (or student loans, ahem) doesn't resolve the problem. Only getting real with ourselves does. The whole rest of this workbook is about tools for getting the reality and the ideal in alignment with each other. There are a few things that can work immediately but a lot of this stuff is a series of medium and long term changes.

The exercises in this chapter are exercises designed to shift your thinking and relationship with money and your budget generally. This is the place where we start looking for creative ways to get our spending on essential must-haves down as close as we can to 50% of our budget.

Your Mental Accounting Experiences

You know how I just asked you to put all your spending into categories? Now we're going to learn to think outside those boxes.

One of the biggest hurdles in being better with our finances is something called mental accounting. The term was introduced in 1999 by economics professor Richard Thayer. He defined mental accounting as "the set of cognitive operations used by individuals and households to organize, evaluate, and keep track of financial activities." The term refers to how we treat money differently based on criteria we assign it.

Mental accounting sounds complicated, but it's actually a pretty simple concept. It means we naturally assign all the money we have, expect, or plan to spend into different mental buckets. The problem is that our brains aren't very good at seeing the big picture. We might have a mental bank account for groceries and one for clothes. That's not a problem until we run out of grocery money for the month and stop buying food (and get hungry), even though we're still going ahead and buying the new sweater we wanted. We forget that money is just money and that we can choose how we use it, no matter what we had previously planned.

Let's dig deep into our unconscious accounting and reflect on these questions:

How have you treated different sources of money differently in the past?

Have you made any financial decisions based on mental accounting that you regretted later?

Are there any particular expenses or income sources that come up unexpectedly for you multiple times in a year?

In what areas of your budget are you most likely to do mental accounting that doesn't serve your goals?

What are some ways you can remind yourself to make conscious spending decisions when you have unexpected expenses or income?

Meet Your Needs for Less

Our essential budget must-haves tend to be pretty set-in-stone but there's often some flexibility if you get creative. Are there any expenditures that you can quickly reduce or get rid of without creating undue hardship in your life? (Sharing wifi with your neighbors, bartering professional services, or bike commuting one day a week?) Or are there areas where you can start planning to save on in the longer term, like moving to a cheaper place, or finding a job with a shorter commute? Every little bit helps, here. Keep this page as an ongoing log of ideas to try (and then record how they worked).

MUST-HAVE	CREATIVE WAY TO SAVE	AMOUNT SAVED

Austerity Month

If your spending feels out of control or you don't feel like you have the ability to make small changes, or that those can make a difference, try the financial equivalent of a Whole30 elimination diet. During an austerity month, your goal is to spend as little as possible while still meeting your basic needs. So you still pay for rent and utilities and your phone, pay the minimums on your credit cards and debts, and buy enough healthy food to keep yourself well-fed. But for anything that's non-essential, either skip it or find a creative way to get the same thing for less or for free.

The idea of an austerity month is usually discussed as being a time of self-denial to help us stop overspending. Then it becomes depressing as fuck and we end up getting mad about it and going on a spending binge. Or get so wrapped up in the "making it at home" that we end up spending fifty dollars on the ingredients to make our own chocolate bar rather than just buying one yummy chocolate bar.

I like to think of austerity month as a mindfulness activity. It's a habit reset that helps us connect to which of our spending is worthwhile and which is something we do because we aren't thinking about it. Austerity month is a great challenge, if you approach it in this way.

If you decide to tackle this challenge, pick a month where it's pretty doable (January is popular—everyone is broke and exhausted and burned out on going out anyway).

And then keep track of your "extra" purchases and savings below.

AUSTERITY MONTH SAVINGS

Where did you get creative and save money? Maybe you looked up the free admission day at the museum, or just realized you didn't really *want* to go to happy hour with everyone after work and used austerity month as a reason to beg off.

CREATIVE SAVINGS STRATEGY	AMOUNT SAVED

AUSTERITY MONTH SPENDING

When did you decide to spend money in a way that wasn't strictly necessary but was thoughtful? Were you home for an extended period of time so subscribing to a new streaming service or having groceries delivered was really worthwhile?

NON-ESSENTIAL SPENDING	WHY I SPENT IT	AMOUNT SPENT

Save Money By Doing Instead of Not Doing

One of the fundamental truths about human nature is that it is always easier to start doing something than to stop doing something. Eating poorly? Add the good foods and let the less-healthy stuff find its own way out of your diet. Overly critical? Focus on saying positive things and watch the criticisms wander off on their own.

Same is true with saving money. If you are looking to cut expenses, add new purchases and activities that are free or cheaper to your day and let them naturally replace the stuff you spend money on now. This feels more like a fun challenge rather than deprivation and limitation.

Find three cost-saving activities that you can engage in as an add-on rather than a replacement. This isn't just limited to must-haves. You can choose fun things, like renting a movie and making popcorn (to replace going out), or more serious ones like joining a therapy group that meets over lunch instead of online shopping during that time.

After you've tried them all, check in. Did the budget expenditure you were hoping to reduce show a decrease this week? Might it over time? Was it easier to make the switch using this method? Do you think you can carry forth this method in other ways?

USUAL EXPENDITURE	REPLACEMENT	AMOUNT SAVED

UNFUCK YOUR SAVINGS AND DEBT

So let's say after you worked out your budget, after you pay off all your must-have expenses (including the minimums on your credit cards and student loans), you have $100 bucks left for debts and investments. Put that $100 in the emergency fund until you hit the $1000 (or whatever number makes better sense for you). If you have less than $100, put that in, too. Even if it's the 5-spot you found in a pair of jeans you haven't worn in a minute. We're going to put it to work for your future.

In this chapter we'll work to start with whatever amount you can eke out of your monthly spending and get you a savings cushion so you can deal with life's small emergencies. And *then*, we'll make a plan to make sure you can rise to more expected occasions like birthdays, holidays, vacations, and school. And *theeeennnnn* we are going to tackle that debt, which does not stand a chance against the power of your budgeting excellence. So much adulting! But totally worth it. Because no human being should be owned by a credit card or loan company.

Make a Fuck-You Fund

The one thing that all the financial guru peeps agree on is that the first money you set aside should be an emergency fund. Not paying down your debt, not investing. Just having some fundage for when life hands you a shit sandwich.

The generally agreed upon number is $1000. A thousand bucks will usually cover your auto insurance co-pay if you're in an accident, or the deposit on a new place if your living situation becomes untenable. Depending on how these types of expenses run in your area, a bit more than a grand might make sense.

Build this fund first, before you do any work toward paying down unsecured debt. Otherwise, the next time a crisis hits, it's going back on a high interest rate credit card or payday loan or some other capitalistic dumpster fire and you are even deeper in the hole we are trying to crawl out of.

We're going to start with that extra $100 a month (or less, or more) that you found in your budget for this category. If you have to skip a month of saving, don't give up—pick it up again next month. You're creating something that wasn't there before. And if you suddenly need a root canal and need to spend everything you've saved... that's what it was there for (this is one of the hardest things for me to remember, I feel that frustration in my soul). Start again, and give yourself a high five for not needing to put that on a credit card.

A lot of financial people say (and I agree) that you shouldn't abandon the emergency fund once you hit your savings mark. I'd continue socking away money into it, in much smaller amounts, while you pay down debt. Like maybe $10 or so. Set a new goal, like having three months of living expenses at your fingertips in case the shit hits the fan, and build towards it slowly.

FUCK-YOU FUND THERMOMETER

We're going to use an old fashioned thermometer to work towards your Fuck You Fund goal. Grab some colored pencils, crayons, the dry erase marker you jacked from work, or whatever you have, and add to the total saved each time you hit a new milestone. .

$1000

$100

Sinking Funds for Special Occasions

Once you have your emergency fund, you may need to jump right ahead to focusing on paying down debt. But if that's not on fire, or there is a little breathing room for more than one thing at a time, another thing to look at is saving towards regular but larger expenses like birthdays, holidays, vacations, fixing the roof, and your value-based goals, like a class you want to take. Remember those bigger-ticket items in your dream budget? That's what this money is for.

In the finance world, this is called a "sinking fund," referring to a pool of money that is set aside for something outside of everyday expenditures. "Sinking" sounds weird and rude. In the finance world, borrowing money for a big ticket expense is called "floating" (kinda like asking someone to float you a tenner for lunch). Setting up a sinking fund is the opposite of borrowing now for something and paying later. Make sense? At least kinda?

More often than not, our budgets get blown on things we know are coming. And we can soften the blow if we plan ahead. If not formally with a sinking fund, informally by stretching out the purchases over the rest of the year based on the budget you put together now. If this is a sure-as-shit expense coming at you in the next few months, planning for it should def be a top priority. If the roof is whimpering but can hold off a minute, focusing on debts first may make more sense.

Here are some budget planners to help you figure out your sinking fund needs.

BACK TO SCHOOL BUDGET PLANNER

ITEMS	AMOUNT
Clothes	
Shoes	
Bookbag	
Computer	
Textbooks	
Notebooks	
Pencils/pens	
Other	
Other	
Other	
Total needed:	
Date needed by:	
Weeks until needed:	
Total needed divided by weeks:	

This last number is the amount you need to set aside each week to make this goal. Is this realistic? If not, adjust your spending plans above until you know you can save for all of them.

BACK TO SCHOOL THERMOMETER

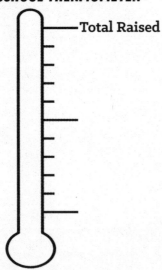

Total Raised

HOLIDAY OR BIRTHDAY BUDGET PLANNER

ITEMS	AMOUNT
Food:	
Dinner at home	
Cake/treats	
Drinks for party/dinner	
Meals out	
Contributions for potlucks	
Gifts:	
Child(ren)	
Friend(s)	
Partner(s)	
Donations	
Other:	
Gift wrapping/supplies	
Decorations/ornaments	
Travel	
Other:	
Other:	
Other:	
Total needed:	
Date needed by:	
Weeks until needed:	
Total needed divided by weeks:	

HOLIDAY THERMOMETER

Total Raised

TRAVEL THERMOMETER

Total Raised

TRAVEL BUDGET PLANNER

You might want to consider making a separate worksheet and breaking down your expected spending by day, especially if your travel includes multiple destinations.

ITEMS	AMOUNT
Transportation	
Getting there and home	
Taxis, intercity travel, etc.	
Lodging	
Food	
Shopping	
Tours/sightseeing	
Other	
Luggage	
Insurance	
Guide books/maps	
Emergency fund	
Other	
Other	
Total needed:	
Date needed by:	
Weeks until needed:	
Total needed divided by weeks:	

Pay Down Your Debt

Once you've got your basic Fuck You Fund laid down, let's look at what to do next with that $100 a month, or however much you have budgeted towards savings and debt.

First, let's list out all your unsecured debt. Here we're looking at credit cards, overdue hospital bills, student loans, etc. We're not looking at your mortgage or car payments.

DEBT	APR	MINIMUM PAYMENT	PAY-OFF AMOUNT

Next we'll use this list to decide how to prioritize your pay-off plan. There are a couple good options, commonly known as the snowball and avalanche debt repayment plans. Take a look and decide which one is right for you.This last number is the amount you need to set aside each week to make this goal. Is this realistic? If not, adjust your spending plans above until you know you can save for all of them.

SNOWBALL PLAN

The snowball plan helps you see progress more and more quickly which is both soothing and motivating for further change. This is the plan that was made popular by Dave Ramsey (and most financial advisors agree with his advice, it's generally on point).

Start with the debt you owe the least on. Add your savings/debt budget (that hypothetical $100 a month) on top of the minimum payment of that smallest debt and keep paying the minimum on the rest. Once that is knocked out, you put your $100 plus the minimum payment from the first debt, which you are no longer paying, into the next smallest one and so on, with the amount you're able to put towards your debts growing every time.

1. List your debts from smallest to largest. Include name and total owed.

2. List your monthly payment due under Minimum Payment Due

3. Decide how much extra you can put towards your debt every month.

4. For the first debt, carry the minimum payment due into the Debt Snowball Amount column.

5. Add that to the extra cash you can pay towards your debt in the 4th column to get the Monthly Snowball Amount.

6. Now divide the total owed (column 2) by the Monthly Snowball Amount (column 4) to get the "Months Til Paid Off".

7. Once you finish paying off your first debt, repeat steps 4-6 with the second debt, also adding the minimum payment from the first debt into the extra cash section.

DEBT NAME	TOTAL OWED	MIN PAYMENT DUE	DEBT SNOWBALL AMOUNT	MONTHS TIL PAID OFF
			Min Payment + Extra Cash = Monthly Snowball Amount to Pay	

AVALANCHE PLAN

In this payment plan, you focus on the debt that is accumulating the most interest first. If you have debt with some redonk-high interest rates, this one may make the most financial sense because it will save you more in the long run.

This is less yummy for our brains in the short term, because you don't see the pay-off progress as fast. But if you calculate the interest you are saving, that may help your motivation level.

Choose that first debt (or your total amount of debt, if you want to think long-term) and color in this thermometer as you move towards wiping it out.

DEBT NAME	TOTAL OWED	MIN PAYMENT DUE	DEBT AVALANCHE AMOUNT	INTEREST RATE	MONTHS UNTIL PAID OFF

DEBT REPAYMENT THERMOMETER

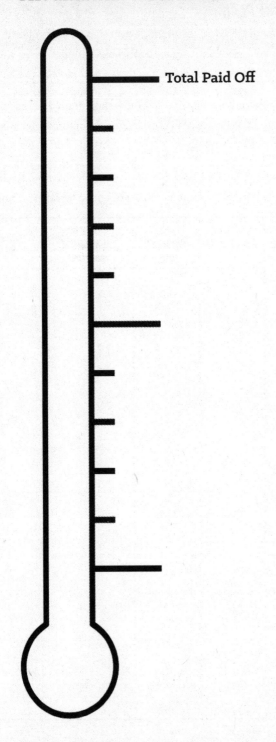

Total Paid Off

UNFUCK YOUR SPENDING ON FUN STUFF

This should be the easy part, right? But I've seen people (and by *people*, I mean *me*) have the hardest time with this category. Since it's fun, it becomes mindless. While yes, I do entirely agree in the Church of Everlasting Life and Treating Oneself, I do also believe that these treats need to stick within a certain portion of our budget (ideally, 30%).

This is the time to think about what you truly enjoy the most and prioritize that. If you love having a nice barista make your coffee for you in the morning, that's totally cool...make that a priority. If you are lusting after a new smart watch, though, making your espresso stovetop can allow you to sock away the fun money to get one.

Do you want to travel more? Do you like being able to splurge on new shoes? Do you do better if you go to a gym to work out versus work out at home? Do you like seeing movies in the theatre or are you fine with whatever is on Netflix? Think about the stuff that makes you happy and weigh those things against each other just like any other aspect of your budget. This will help you not overspend *and* lessen your FOMO.

100 Things You Would Do if Money Were No Object

This is a space to just spitball. Yes, I totally want you to list 100. It's way harder than it looks!

After you go through the list, highlight or put a star next to the ones that you are most excited or passionate about. Should any of these items go on your long term savings plan so you can start reaching for at least a couple of these goals?

1.

2.

3.

4.

5.

6.

7.

8.

9.

10.

11.

12.

13.

14.

15.

16.

17.

18.

19.

20.

21.

22.

23.

24.

25.

26.

27.

28.

29.

30.

31.

32.

33.

34.

35.

36.

37.

38.

39.

40.

41.

42.

43.

44.

45.

46.

47.

48.

49.

50.

51.

52.

53.

54.

55.

56.

57.

58.

59.

60.

61.

62.

63.

64.

65.

66.

67.

68.

69.

70.

71.

72.

73.

74.

75.

76.

77.

78.

79.

80.

81.

82.

83.

84.

85.

86.

87.

88.

89.

90.

91.

92.

93.

94.

95.

96.

97.

98.

99.

100.

Treating Oneself Well and Often, but, Alas, with Well Defined Limits

First of all, go back to your dream budget list and copy off all the "fun stuff" items you had added.

Ok, cool. So now I want you to rank everything on that list as a 1, 2, or 3. 1 being highest priority, 2 is a mid-range fun having thing, and 3 as a lowest priority. Got it? Now, list the first three "1" items below along with its estimated monthly cost:

Fun Thing:

Super Fun Thing:

Also Deeply Cool:

Now where is your budget at? Room to add some more "1"s? Go ahead and budget them out below:

Totally Free Stuff that Makes Your Life Better

You don't have to spend any money at all to do so much stuff that connects to your values and self-care plans. Here are some ideas to get you started and plenty of space to write in your own favorites for when you need a reminder.

- Take a walk

- Explore social media hashtags on a topic that you are passionate about

- Interact with a cute cat or dog (even if it's just an online video)

- Start a conversation

- Masturbate

- Rearrange your furniture, clean out your junk drawer, reorganize your hot sauce shelf

- Check out the "new arrivals" shelf at the library

-

-

-

-

-

-

-

-

-

-

Awesome Stuff that Costs Less than $10

I have definitely been in a place where I didn't even have ten dollars to spend (hence the worksheet above)...but a lot of times we don't have the money to do what's on the dream list, so we get grumbly. And sometimes getting ourselves out of the grumble-slumps can be accomplished by spending a little bit of our fun money on something that's...well...actually fun. Try these and keep an ongoing list of cheap thrills that work for you.

- Get a drink and a treat at a local coffee shop and sit in the park and enjoy it with a book or magazine.

- Check out your local thrift shop and see if you can find one piece of clothing you love

- Donate $10 to a cause that you are passionate about.

-

-

-

-

-

-

-

-

-

-

-

-

Managing the Impulsive Buying Habit

What are your spending triggers? Do you shop when you feel like crap? When you're scrolling social media? When you've had a glass of wine? When you are out with friends and they encourage you to buy the thing you are hesitant about? If you have credit cards in hand? (Yes, research does demonstrate that we will literally spend double what we intended to spend if we are using plastic instead of paper, and that's before the interest charges rack up).

Be your own responsibility wing-man and put safeties in place to help you not slide into spending habits that don't align with your other goals and values. It's okay to get creative when we are fighting for our longer term goals in the face of our short term discomfort and desires.

Next time the impulse-buy gremlins sneak past your wingman of responsibility, check in with yourself:

Thing you want to buy:

Is this purchase in line with my budget?

Is this purchase in line with my goals?

Will buying this thing fuck everything the fuck up?

Do I need this?

If it's a want, will it bring a measure of joy to my life?

Is it something I can easily afford?

If I think better of it later, can I easily return it or am I fucked?

If I wait a week or a month to buy it, will I still want it just as much?

Am I feeling impulsive or crappy or off kilter and looking for ways to feel better?

If I feel crappy, is there anything else I can do to make myself feel better first?

Is there anything else I need to think through?

UNFUCKING TOGETHER

Your personal finances don't exist in a vacuum. Maybe you've got a partner, family, kids, roommates, coworkers, friends. This chapter contains exercises to help you with those conversations about money that can be so difficult, whether you're trying to make a savings plan with a reluctant parent or negotiating better terms with a debt collector.

Another great way to make your relationship with money more healthy is to foster open conversations about it with people you trust, whether that's regular check-ins with a partner or starting a club with friends to work towards your mutual goals.

Don't forget to think about your boundaries, too. You don't have to spill all your financial info to anyone who asks (or even to people who tell you theirs). You get to decide what is comfortable and safe for you.

Your Money Communication Boundaries

Boundaries are the lines we draw between what belongs to other people and what belongs to ourselves. Obviously, money conversations have a lot to do with boundaries. (In my book *Unfuck Your Boundaries*, I go into a lot more detail that may be helpful if you think that you have a lot of boundary issues around money... your purchase supports the wet foods habits of my asshole cats.) One big idea I'd like to give you here is the idea of boundary styles: Rigid, permeable, and flexible.

Rigid boundaries are boundaries that nothing gets through, ever. When it comes to money, a rigid boundary might be a family rule that nobody ever talks about money, or it might be a personal habit of refusing to buy something new until the old thing is well and truly worn-out, even if it doesn't really work the way you need it to. Sometimes you need rigid boundaries, like if someone is sponging off you, or you're being pursued by an aggressive marketer.

Permeable boundaries are boundaries that everything gets through if it wants to. Permeable boundaries around money might look like not being able to refuse when someone asks you for a loan even if you really can't afford it or don't want to do it, or being unable to resist a strong sales pitch. Sometimes you need permeable boundaries, like if you have to do whatever you need to survive an emergency.

Flexible boundaries are goals for most situations. These come from listening to our internal voice that knows what is safe for us, but also wants us to experience growth. Flexible boundaries might lead us to make informed choices about large purchases that go against our inclination to save, or might show us a creative way to help our struggling family member by paying their bills directly for a month instead of the loan they asked for.

What are some of your boundaries around money (earning, spending, saving, etc)?

How are your boundaries around money similar to or different from the ones you learned growing up?

In general, are the majority of your boundaries around money rigid, permeable, or flexible?

Which of your boundaries around money are rigid right now? Are there any that need to be challenged? Are there any that need to be more rigid?

Which of your boundaries around money are permeable right now? Are there any that need to be strengthened into being flexible or even rigid? Do you have any that should remain permeable? If so, how does that permeability serve you in your life right now?

What would your ideal boundary balance around money be? How close are you to that ideal right now?

What is something actively in your control that you can do to move towards your ideal balance?

THINK

Financial conversations can be stressful and triggering and quickly turn into fights. It helps to bring your best self to the table instead of your scared, defensive, and reactionary self. Because in the end, it should be the two of you against the problem instead of the two of you against each other.

THINK is a "best self" skill you can use in all sorts of financial conversations: with family, partners, your boss, your landlord, the bank teller, even with yourself. It comes from a theoretical orientation I borrow from on the regular, dialectical behavioral therapy. Developed by Marsha Linehan to help individuals with borderline personality disorder (BPD) better self regulate, it matches traditional cognitive techniques with mindfulness and distress tolerance based skills.

Since developed, it's been shown to be effective in many different situations. And one of the core areas that DBT focuses on is interpersonal effectiveness. That is, maintaining a clear understanding of our own boundaries, and attending to our wants and needs, while respecting the other person and the relationship itself. DBT is a skills-based approach that uses alot of acronyms to help frame the skills.

One of the interpersonal effectiveness skills I use often is the THINK skill, because it is specifically designed as a tool to not only communicate effectively with a partner, but also keep from dumping a ton of negative emotions into the conversation even when upset. Like every skill, it's easier to practice using it before you're in a negative place. After a while it will become second nature to communicate using THINK, which will make arguments far easier to manage.

T stands for "**THINK**." Yup, super original. But hey, the thoughtful part of our brain can shut down when we are upset. And in this case it means think of the other person's perspective on the issue. Where are they coming from? Do they see it in a different way from you?

H stands for "**HAVE EMPATHY**." Empathy is different from sympathy. It doesn't mean "feel sorry for," it means really connecting to the other person's emotional experience. Remember to connect to their emotional content, not just your own.

I stands for "**INTERPRET THEIR BEHAVIOR**." And let your imagination take over. You can start with the most irrational, ridiculous thing possible ("They totally schemed to fuck me over...it is part of their master, evil plan of world domination!") to the more reasonable. ("Their behavior wasn't thoughtful, but it wasn't intentionally hurtful.") Starting with the the most extreme seems counterintuitive, but it burns off some steam and helps connect us to how over-reactive we can be when upset... which allows us to more easily accept a rational interpretation.

N stands for "**NOTICE**." This means simply notice how your partner is responding and interacting. Notice when they are trying to make improvements. Notice their reaction to you. Notice the other things going on in their life that are operating as either positives or negatives. Pay attention to where they are at, not just where you are at.

K stands for "**KINDNESS**." Even if you are having to make a hard decision or hold firm to a boundary doesn't mean you have to be mean, right? And honestly, consistency and firmness are also a form of kindness. And you can express that in words, as well as actions. "Fuck off and leave me alone." isn't kind. But "I'm not going anywhere, and I know we will work through this but right now I need some time to calm down so we can discuss it more effectively." is kind. It maintains commitment and attachment, and expresses a needed boundary and break from a difficult situation, while taking responsibility for the need.

I Statements

Any time we communicate about highly emotional stuff (like money) it's important to take responsibility for our own feelings and experiences. One way to do that is through how we communicate. For example, it's a common habit to say "you made me angry." But nobody has control over your anger but you.

"I statement" communication, on the other hand, invokes a language of responsibility for our own emotional content, while sharing with others how their behavior has informed our emotional content.

Communicating in this way is going to feel weird and difficult at first, because it simply isn't how people discuss their emotions in this country. Practicing helps. I statements can be used in all sorts of situations, with your closest loved ones and complete strangers.

My favorite story is the client I had years ago who started her I statement by saying "I feel you're being an asshole!" Funny as hell. Also, not an I statement.

Some better examples:

I feel anxious when it isn't made clear in advance if we have to cover our own lunch at business meetings. What I want is for management to make a clear policy about this so I can budget accordingly or make alternative plans for my meal.

Extra credit for explaining the "why" of what you're feeling, like this:

I feel frustrated and hurt when you go out for lunch every day even though we agreed to save that money for our move. I feel good when I know we are working together towards our shared goal of getting out of this shitty apartment.

Or:

I felt uncomfortable when you asked me to spot you money again at the restaurant in front of our other friends. I said yes because I don't want to embarrass you or make anyone else uncomfortable, but I really don't have the money to spend. I need you to speak to me privately ahead of time if you are hoping I can float you a loan.

Depending on the circumstances, you can even take an extra step in acknowledging that they didn't intend the distress you felt, e.g. *"I know you had no way of knowing I'm tight on cash this month, but..."* This can go a long way to disarming a potential fight.

Try this with your partner, family member, coworker, or friend. Here's a good chance to practice using some of the more common issues that come up for you and the people you have to communicate with on a regular basis.

I feel _____

when you _____

What I want is _____

I feel _____

when you _____

What I want is _____

I feel _____

when you _____

What I want is _____

I feel _____

when you _____

What I want is _____

I feel _____

when you _____

What I want is _____

I feel _____

when you _____

What I want is _____

I feel _____

when you _____

What I want is _____

I feel _____

when you _____

What I want is _____

Your Values in Partnership

Have you ever had a conversation about something that seemed really silly on the surface, but it turned into a super-passionate or angry argument? Chances are, both of you were activated over an underlying value. It wasn't the surface disagreement that got you heated up, but what you hold as important in the world. Isn't it amazing how often this kind of fight is about money?

Figuring out where your values overlap and where they differ, can go a long way in helping you focus your financial goals. This exercise is for getting at what big picture life values are most important to both you and your partner (your romantic partner, business partner, sibling, or anyone else you share financial responsibilities with).

Take a look through the values list in the "Values Clarification" exercise. Each of you can choose your top 3 or 5 or 10, however many you want. Put the ones you share in the center of the diagram on the next page and the ones you separately hold close in the non-overlapping parts.

Talk about what values you agree on and how you can align your shared activities to be true to those. It might also be helpful to talk about the ones you each hold separately and your reasons for those.

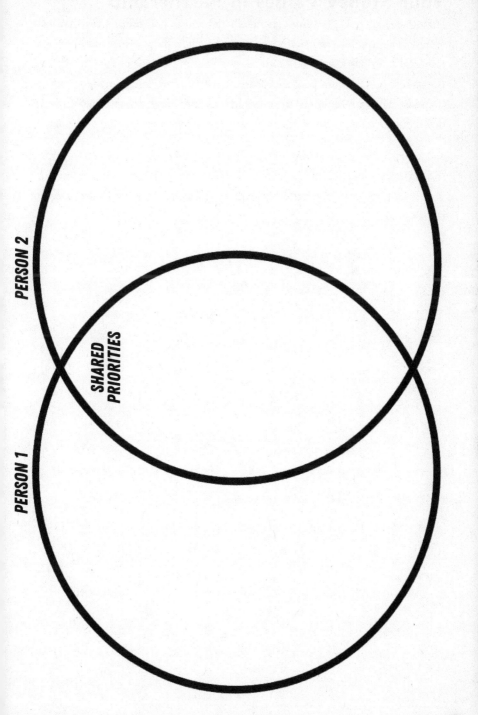

PERSON 2

PERSON 1

SHARED PRIORITIES

Your Money Values in Partnership

Now that you've worked through the shared values and differences that steer your decision-making processes, let's hone in on how those values influence your financial priorities. Go to the "Your Money Values" exercise in the Unfuck Your Budget chapter. Each of you, choose the 3, 5, 10, or however many feels right as the most important financial priorities in your life. Put the ones you both wrote down in the center, and the others in your respective circles on the next page.

Again, start the conversation with the priorities you share. How can you work to maximize those? Then talk about the basis you each have for the priorities you hold separately. It'll probably help you understand each other in future disagreements.

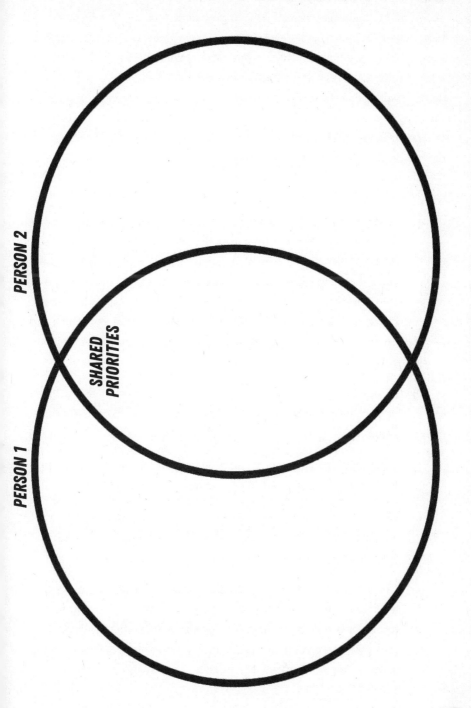

PERSON 2

PERSON 1

SHARED PRIORITIES

Start a Money Club

One of the big challenges around unfucking our money and worth is that *we don't talk about it*. Starting a money club gives you a peer group to bounce ideas off of, learn together, and build in a little gentle accountability. Money clubs can work a lot of different ways—working towards a common goal (like paying off your debts) or just talking about what's going on with you financially and your progress through the exercises in this book. Or you could start a club where you actually put money in towards helping one member at a time achieve their financial goals, or investing in a cause or person together.

Some ideas to get you started:

1) What do you want the dynamics of the group to be? Open to anyone that is interested or do you want to include/invite people who are maybe in the same financial place that you are in? People who live in your area? Have the same career goals? A BIPOC specific group? All individuals who are trans* or non-binary? (Creating a group of people who are facing similar experiences and barriers doesn't make you shitty and exclusive… it may make complete sense and may help you shape group goals and topics in a different way.)

2) How often do you want to meet and what is the meeting format? Live or by chat or texting? In person? Google Hangouts or Zoom? Facebook group? A GroupMe or Slack accountability group?

3) What topics do you want to focus on, at least for the first few groups. Budgeting? Savings? Investing? Creating a small business?

4) Do you want to have special guests join in? For example, do you want a financial advisor join and discuss options (knowing that they are also pimping their services)?

5) Do you want to look at group investments? There are groups that are formed in which the expectation is that everyone puts in money into an investment pool and then everyone splits the dividends. This minimizes the investment risk but then you also may be stuck investing in something you don't want to invest in…or you may not be in a place to invest at all.

UNFUCK YOUR

WORK

Working with unfucking our spending and savings and budgets in general is all well and good...but if our income is complete bullshit there may not be much wiggle room in that regard. Or maybe we're making slamming money, but in a job that is so shitty and soul sucking it has eaten away at our self-worth to the point that the paycheck isn't really serving anything anymore.

Labor and worth and money are all tethered together for most of us, and issues surrounding work can really affect our mental health, so this chapter is all about getting our work lives in order. Maybe that means asking for a raise or negotiating a change in job duties. Maybe it means getting a new job entirely, ideally one with better pay and a less crappy commute. Maybe it means getting our work lives better aligned with our values, or remembering what we cared about to begin with when we started out doing what we're doing. Or maybe it means finding some new side hustles or even monetizing our joy.

Find Your Meaning

The best way I've found to approach a job change or career switch is to focus on what engagement looks like at a personal level. What actually matters to you?

Work doesn't have to be self-actualizing. You don't have to super love your job and find all your meaning in doing it. If work is the thing that pays the bills and you don't give AF about it otherwise that's totally fine. But a lot of people do wish they could align their work with how they live the rest of their lives. It takes planning and creativity but is more doable than we sometimes realize, especially when feeling super stuck in a crap fast-food gig. The planning and creativity part comes after we get a little unstuck and start thinking about the possibilities and potential there might be out there for us.

These questions are important ones to look at *before* planning for a switch. I have seen people jump from one hellscape job into the dumpster fire of another, because they were so desperate to leave the hellscape that they didn't see where they were going. Different isn't necessarily better. Or you might find that your current work does align with your values, but something important about it needs to change.

Reflect on these questions:

Would you work if you didn't have to?

Would it be the same work that you are doing now? If so, how would it be different?

What kinds of work situations do you find yourself in where you work harder than you have to?

What kinds of activities are most likely to make you think "THIS. This is my contribution to making the world suck less?"

Are there any situations where you would work for less than you make now? What makes those situations different for you?

What kinds of things do you do when you have free time and no obligations?

If you were able to schedule your working time any way you would like, what would your weekly calendar look like?

What are you known for at work, among your family, among your friends? Like, what are the go-to types of problems that people rely on you to solve or assist them with solving?

What Can You Control About Your Livelihood?

In *Unfuck Your Worth*, I talk a lot about finding your "right livelihood," which is part of the eightfold path of Buddhism. That sounds super fancy and deep, but it is really just a way of becoming conscious of what your work contributes to the world. What does it support for your community, for your family, and within you? Right livelihood helps us look at what is in our control in any work situation... which is another super fancy and deep way of saying *how can we keep our minds right when our jobs suck?*

When we focus on what is within our ability to control, we can use that information to shape our right livelihood. So in the space below, write in what is in your control and what is outside of your control in relation to your work.

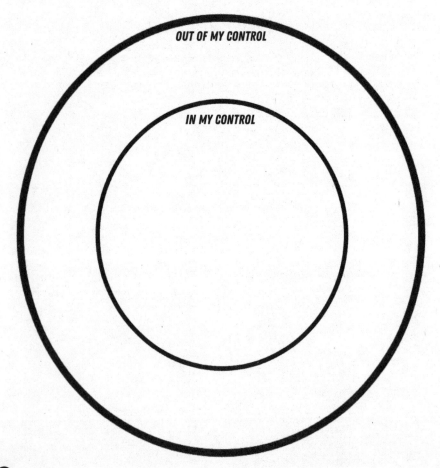

Know Your Worth

How much income *should* you be earning? How much is your time and energy and labor worth?

I mean, the capitalistic hellmouth literally runs on maximizing profit. And maximizing profit means minimizing expenses. Including human labor. Rare is the place that is going to appropriately compensate you without a damn battle.

Add to that, the fact that those of us who work in not-for-profits, community agencies, and the like are there because we value being of service more than making fuck-tons of money….and while a lot of these agencies are legitamately running on a shoe-string, many more are taking advantage of their workers, knowing that they are huge-hearted humans who are passionate about the work they are doing.

I want you to push out of that modesty zone and *go to town* on why you are an utter bad-ass at the work you do.

What do you bring to the table? List everything, large and small.

Education and Training:

Experience:

Hustle:

Personality traits and other cool shit that enhance your workplace value (creative problem solver, likeable, schedule flexibility, etc.):

Regular job duties ...like every-damn-thing at work you are responsible for:

The extra stuff you do that you aren't even responsible for but you do anyway because you're a badass like that:

What Next? Why Next? When Next?

Are you thinking (either wistfully or get-me-the-fuck-outfully) it might be time to go for that promotion or move on to a new job or even a whole new career? Trust Auntie Faith (that is, learn from her mistakes) about being proactive instead of reactive. Take some time to look at what a switch might entail. Write it out, make a vision board, use the goal setting worksheet at the end of this book, or do whatever works best for you, but get a real plan down on paper.

Contemplate these questions:

What sounds good? New job? Same company or a different one? Whole new career or field?

What is the impetus for the change?

What would it take to make this change happen?

What is the best-case scenario payoff?

What is the worst-case scenario?

What is the most likely outcome of a change?

Still thinking this might be a good plan?

What's the first step to making this real?

Career Exploration

Use this worksheet to help explore new career directions.

First, write down anything you know you need out of a job—the hard limits.

Wage/salary requirement:

Hours requirements:

Location requirements:

Industries you cannot condone:

Job tasks you can't do, like lifting heavy things or driving:

Other dealbreakers:

Now list fields that seem appealing to you to explore:

Now research actual job openings in those fields. Write the job titles below and then comb the listings for whether or not your dealbreaker conditions are met.

Into the Nightmare

Imagine your nightmare job. Imagine it in great detail. Write about it.

Now imagine anything you could do to make this unsuitable job bearable, even just a little. What would give it meaning for you? For instance, maybe your nightmare job is working at a meat processing plant, but it would become a little more tolerable if you could join a union-organizing effort.

How can you apply these strategies to your current work, or use them to figure out your next work decision?

What's Your Side Hustle?

Side hustles are a reality for most of us. The extra money can be used for a lot of things: to make ends meet; to be able to save for a trip; to get ahead of our debt. All that important shit. They allow flexibility in a system that doesn't support a fuller range of choices for most people.

Maybe your side hustle is extra on top of your regular job. Maybe it's what's helping you get by at all, or maybe it's helping you save up for the security to take a big leap. Maybe your side hustle is your main hustle, allowing you to be home for your kids, or care for an ailing partner, or have the flexibility to work on your music, or manage your chronic illness. Or maybe your income is cobbled together from various side hustles, for money and barter.

The important thing is to consider how much time we have to devote to side hustles, and choosing stuff that won't burn us out even further. Once you decide on something, it's worth going through the "Is it a scam" worksheet in the last chapter of this workbook, especially if it's a sales or multi-level marketing type gig.

If you are considering a side hustle, here's a worksheet to help you think through your options:

List out all the potential side hustles you've thought about.

Google for more side hustle ideas. Anything sound interesting that you hadn't thought of? Bonus points for fun and/or rewarding? Rank out the few that seem the most intriguing.

Research what the up-front investment cost would be for the most appealing one.

Do some research on how much money people are ACTUALLY making.

What about the time factor? How much time could you devote to this project without damaging your physical and mental health or having to de-prioritize your relationships or other important stuff?

What will be your next step?

Monetizing Your Joy

Maybe you've decided to make your art, craft, or hobby your next career or side-hustle. Obviously there are tons of business considerations that would have to be taken into account (and plenty of people have written those books). But before building the structure of that business, there's other considerations that should come first.

What's your joy? Meaning, what's your creative outlet that people keep telling you *"OMG you should totally sell those, I would buy them?"*

What would be the benefits of turning your joy into a business or side-hustle?

What would be the possible downside?

What kind of investment would you need to make in order to start (not just financial investment in supplies and the like, but investment in your time and energy, too)?

Is that an investment that would make sense in your life right now?

How would you measure success in this enterprise? (e.g., I'm enjoying myself, I make at least XX amount of money per craft show I do, etc.)

How would you know that you want to discontinue this effort? (e.g., I'm losing sleep to keep up with the workload, that I am having to undervalue my work to match the current market, etc.)

FINANCIAL SAFETY

Not all money problems are created equal. This section is about figuring out if your money issues are putting you or others in danger, whether you're in a financially abusive relationship, in danger of falling for a scam, or have an addiction or mental illness piece that needs immediate attention.

Recognizing Financial Abuse

Financial abuse is a form of coercive control. While it doesn't leave any visible marks on our bodies, it is one of the most effective ways of abusing and controlling another human being. We think of abuse as being physical, but research demonstrates that it's control and manipulation that cause the most trauma in those of us who have been abused.

Controlling the money controls the relationship. The most obvious indicator of financial abuse is the direct control of household resources, but it can also look like the control of other aspects of your life that impact your financial autonomy.

Go down this checklist and see if any of these apply to your relationship (whether it's a partnership, family relationship, caretaking situation, or even a roommate). If this is something you are dealing with in the present, I hope you approach your situation like you would any other abusive situation and find ways to be safe, whether you plan to leave or decide to stay. The next exercise will help you make a plan.

◯ Bank accounts being managed by only one person, with the other person being either given an allowance, brought shopping, or having to ask for money for any purchases, no matter who is producing the income

◯ Major decisions about family income being made by only one person

- [ ] All assets being in the name of and/or controlled by one person (mortgage, rental agreement, cars, etc.)

- [ ] Controlling access to medical care

- [ ] Controlling use of contraceptives or STI prevention methods

- [ ] Interfering with or threatening your immigration/citizenship status

- [ ] Creating other legal trouble for you

- [ ] Threatening your housing stability (e.g., threatening to kick you out of a home they pay for, breaking rules set in a home rental to have your lease terminated and get you both evicted)

- [ ] Keeping you from work/makes you late to work/disrupts your workday/gets you fired

- [ ] Destroying your property

- [ ] Destroying the property of your friends and family

- [ ] Anything else that causes you a level of financial strain that you cannot afford

Creating a Financial Safety Plan

One of the best things you can do for yourself if you find yourself in a financially abusive situation is make a plan for getting safe.

There are a ton of good resources out there if you need to create a big, general safety plan. Start by using your browser to search for "domestic violence safety plan." Some websites with good resources include the National Domestic Violence Hotline, the National Coalition Against Domestic Violence, and WomensLaw.org (and no, they serve peoples of all genders or lack thereof, not just women).

An extensive safety plan is many pages long, but knowing the financial abuse issues I have seen so many people struggle with, I wanted to create some space here for you to plan specifically around this issue, should it apply to you. Your safety plan will need to be specific to your circumstances. You may have to plan for additional family members or pets. You may have medical issues that will require significant support.

Here are some questions to consider in your personal safety plan

1) What accounts do you have access to? Checking, savings, credit cards? If your name is on an account but you haven't been given access by a partner, do you have the means to regain access? For instance, can you order a new card with your name on it for a shared account?

2) Do you have a safe place to store this account information? Do you have someone you can trust to hold your banking information, back up credit or debit cards, etc.? If you don't have a safe someone, can you hide it somewhere safely in your possession or home (stashed in the freezer or the first aid kit or something)?

3) Can you withdraw cash from these accounts so your spending patterns aren't traced based on card swipes?

4) Do you have any mechanisms for saving some cash or creating a separate account that your abusive partner or family member does not have access to? For example, I have had clients take out a little cash when buying groceries and stash it for their own escape fund. Do you have a safe person who can maintain possession of these assets for

you (especially if its cash)? If not, do you have a way you can hide it somewhere safely in your home?

5) Are there assistance programs in your area that can help you get back on your feet should you choose to leave? Is there a safe place you can keep that information available so you have it if you need to leave in a hurry?

Is Your Shopping a Problem?

In the non-workbook version of Unfuck Your Worth, I get into the science of why shopping addiction doesn't exist as an actual diagnosis. Short version is that it is usually emblematic of something else going on, like anxiety or depression. But looking at how shopping may be problematic can be the first step in seeing how we are using shopping to not deal with the underlying shit.

If these questions are ringing any bells for you, a lot of the budgeting tools earlier in the workbook can be really helpful. The austerity month challenge in particular can be a really good habit disruptor. But any of these exercises should go along with treatment for the underlying issues you are struggling with. Remember that compulsive buying is a symptom of other mental health issues (depression or anxiety being the likely culprits), and you need support in your healing, not just budgeting advice.

Consider these questions as your starting point:

- [ ] Do you prefer to shop alone?

- [ ] Do you shop to avoid uncomfortable or painful feelings?

- [ ] Do you feel better when you purchase something and then guilty later?

- [ ] Do you buy a lot of stuff you don't need and/or end up never using?

- [ ] Do you hide what you are buying from others?

- [ ] Do you lie (outright or by omission) about your purchases or the cost of them?

- [ ] Is your shopping causing financial problems for you (even if just diverting from your other financial goals)?

Do You Have a Gambling Addiction?

Gambling addiction is a real thing. It can be formally diagnosed if you have experienced at least four of the following issues in the past year. If this resonates with you, finding a therapist who specializes in this treatment or a peer recovery group may be helpful to your recovery.

- ◯ You are spending more and more money when gambling in order to achieve the same excitement as before.

- ◯ When you have tried to stop gambling or decrease your gambling, you find yourself to be restless and irritable.

- ◯ When you have tried to stop gambling or decrease your gambling, you have been repeatedly unsuccessful.

- ◯ You think about gambling frequently, such as planning your next gambling experience and mentally revisiting previous experiences, and you are focused on ways of getting money so you can gamble again.

- ◯ When you don't feel well emotionally, you are far more likely to gamble.

- ◯ If you lose money gambling, you want to gamble more in order to even out your losses ("chasing" one's losses).

- ◯ You have had to rely on others to help with gambling related money problems

- ◯ You have lied to conceal your gambling activities.

- ◯ Your gambling has significantly affected another life domain in a negative way, such as losing or jeopardizing a relationship, a job, or an educational opportunity.

If you're concerned about your gambling, here are some resources that can help.

SAMHSA's National Helpline

A confidential, free, 24-hour-a-day, 365-day-a-year, information service, in English and Spanish

1-800-662-HELP (4357)

TTY: 1-800-487-4889

Gamblers Anonymous

12-step abstinence model for gambling addiction

www.gamblersanonymous.org

Gam-Anon International Service

Another 12-step abstinence-based model

https://www.gam-anon.org/

Smart Recovery

12-step alternative based in cognitive behavioral therapy, addresses gambling addiction as well as substance addiction

Smartrecovery.org/gambling-addiction

Avoiding Scams and Pyramid Schemes

There are a lot of businesses out there whose sole purpose is to prey on your financial desperation and/or desire to take ownership of your life by becoming your own boss. Before you invest or wire money, take on a work-from-home gig, or take a call center job, here's a checklist to keep yourself safe

Early possible red flags: Being recruited by another distributor (like at a house party, or someone you haven't talked to since high school DMing you). Being told it's "direct sales." Being told that it's a work from home job with flexible hours and high income potential. Anything that sounds cheerfully vague. Being told your investment will grow quickly. Being rushed into a decision. Only finding the costs in the finest of fine print. The company being brand new or wanting you to work for equity instead of pay.

Get someone on the phone, ask these questions, and write down the answers:

What is the upfront cost or investment?

What are the recurring costs?

How are you paid? How often? Do you have to hit a certain threshold for payout?

Are refunds for unsold products standard practice?

What are the highest, lowest, and most likely amounts of income you could reasonably make in your first month? What are the statistical chances of someone earning at each of those levels?

How much time will you need to invest in your first month in order to make the least and most likely income levels? How much does that pencil out hourly?

Can you afford the worst case scenario from doing this?

Is it multi-level? Meaning, would you make more money by recruiting other people than by selling the products themselves?

What kinds of caveats or complaints do you see when you look the company up? What does the Better Business Bureau have to say about them? Google Reviews?

Imagine telling the most adult, responsible person in your life about this opportunity (or actually tell them)—what's their reaction?

How to Make a Decision

What is my desired outcome?

What is the simplest solution to achieve it? Is there an easier way?

Does my idea work for everybody involved?

Y / N

Are the costs & consequences acceptable?

Y / N

What are the worst, best, and likely outcomes? Can I manage them all?

Y / N

Does this decision cause harm to anyone I care about and/or our relationship?

Y / N

Does this decision take too much time and energy
from the things I want and need to do?

Y / N
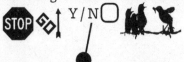

Could this decision cost more money than I can afford? Is there a cheaper way?

Y / N

DO IT!

ACHIEVE YOUR GOALS

In-depth goal setting is essential to this conversation about self-worth. No matter what you're working on—saving up, getting a new job, a move, or a relationship change—you probably have some sense by now of what is the biggest thing you want to work on to get you aligned with your values and dreams.

Getting our goals down into a workable format is what makes them achievable. Winning the lottery would also help, but this is also a good start!

What, exactly, is your goal? What do you desire? State this in positive terms. Not what you don't want but what you really, really want. Choose something that is in your control. Not "I want my partner to stop drinking." You can only control yourself, after all, right?

Now describe your goal in sensory-specific terms. What will you see, hear, and feel when you achieve this goal?

Is this goal achievable? Is this something you can get done? You know, REASONABLY.

So presuming we passed the achievable test, now ask yourself if it is realistic? That is, is it worth your time and commitment. Take some time to jot down notes on the following questions. What sacrifices do I have to make in pursuit of this goal? How will this affect my life in both negative and positive ways? And while you're at it, whose goal is this really? Is it a goal that a parent or partner has encouraged you toward but it isn't really what you want for YOURSELF? If you pursue that goal, then, does it mean that you real goal is to please someone in your life by earning this achievement instead of earning the achievement itself?

Does this goal align with your value system? Think about your moral compass for a moment. Whether it be spiritual or secular. Is what you are wanting to accomplish in alignment with what you consider to be important about who you are and how you interact with the world around you?

What is the timeline for this goal? What's a reasonable amount of time to spend on this? What amount of time are you willing to spend on this?

How will the work you need to put into achieving this goal affect the people around you? What impact will it have on the people who are important in your life. List both positive and negative impacts.

You made a list of things you may lose or give up in the process. Are there any ways of mitigating those losses?

What else will achieving this goal do for you? What are your side gains? If your goal is to go back to school, what will doing so give you other than a new degree or certification?

How will you know when you've achieved this goal? If your goal is moving to a new city, that's easy. When you are in the new city, you've achieved your goal. But answering this question can be way harder than it looks, right? When people tell me, for example, that their goal is to be happy and I ask them to explain what happy looks like, I usually get feedback like "I want to have a positive relationship with my partner and enjoy my career. To me, those are goals are more about being connected and fulfilled than happy. When you start looking at your markers of achievement, you may realize that your goal wording needs to shift somewhat. Good deal. Go ahead and shift away.

Why have you not achieved this goal already? What has gotten in your way in the past?

What obstacles are still in your path in the present? What obstacles may come up in the future?

Which of these obstacles do you have control over? What is your plan for managing them?

Which obstacles are out of your control? What resources can you use to work around them?

Who can help you or be an accountability partner for you?

What have you done already that is moving you in the direction of achieving this goal?

What would be the next step?

What is your action plan and time line for taking the next step?

After completing this step, what did you learn? Is there anything you need to shift after this point of action?

Based on what you completed already, and what you learned in the process, what's the next step? (This is the place where you lather, rinse, repeat through goal completion.)

CONCLUSION

Since this workbook is designed to get you started, not to operate as the encyclopedia of finance or substitute for an accounting degree, you may be kinda exhausted but now realizing you aren't nearly done.

Well, shit, that was a pleasant thought.

Ahem. Let's try that again.

So, now you have done the hard part of getting started and now you have the momentum to keep doing the difficult work!

Much better.

But in all seriousness, getting started really is the most difficult part of any difficult change. Change requires new habit building in order to wire new neural pathways in our brains. We have to do it in a very intentional and mindful way for the first few months. It's exhausting and feels like it takes *so much fucking time.*

But after a while, it just becomes the thing we do. So say a year from now you want to put together a business plan for starting your own company. It will require some research and focus but it won't be nearly as emotionally exhausting because now, to invoke Glennon Doyle, you know how to do hard things.

So this is only a conclusion of *this* workbook, it's not the conclusion of your work on financial literacy and self-worth. Go keep exploring, settling into yourself, and finding ways to navigate your life as authentically as possible.

ABUNDANCE THINKING

"There will always be more"

Collaborates

Gives generously

Freely offers help
and information

Trusts and builds rapport

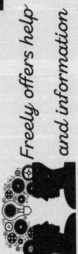

SCARCITY THINKING

"There will never be enough"

Competes

Hoards

Won't share information

Doesn't offer help

Strives to grow

Believes that the best is yet to come

Sees that the pie is growing

Thinks big

Embraces risk

Takes ownership of change

Fears being replaced

Believes times are tough

Believes that the pie is disappearing

Thinks small

Avoids risk

Fears change

Suspects others

COMMON BRAIN TRAPS

Cognitive distortions are ways that our mind convinces us of something that isn't true. These irrational thoughts are a common cause of maladaptive coping and toxic behaviors, used to reinforce negative thinking or emotions. We send ourselves bad data and convince ourselves that it's true. Then they keep us feeling bad about ourselves.

Always Being Right: You must constantly "prove" yourself to be correct even when it hurts others' feelings.

Fallacy of Change: You wait on social power structures to force someone else to do what

Blaming: You can't see your own problems, influence, or contributions. Everything is someone else's fault.

Fallacy of Fairness: You find others guilty when they don't follow your code of justice.

Disqualifying the Positive: You dismiss every inch of praise as undeserved, an attempt at flattery, or naïveté.

Jumping to Conclusions: You make negative assumptions with little or no evidence.

Emotional Reasoning: You believe that negative feelings expose the "true" nature of things and that reality is a reflection of emotionally linked thoughts.

Filtering: You exclude information that does not conform to your already held beliefs and focus entirely on

Mind Reading: You "know" that others must be thinking the worst possible things about you so you find no point in trying in making effort.

Labeling and Mislabeling: You judge someone's entire character and on a single mistake as judge and through your own values.

Magnification and Minimization: You make mountains out of molehills or vice versa.

Catastrophizing: You expect that unlikely, worst possible outcomes will come true.

Overgeneralization: You make broad judgments hastily without sufficient data. Every single event implies consistency.

Personalization: You put responsibility on someone (often yourself) who had no control over the events in question.

Should Statements: You believe that the same rules always create the same outcomes; no other factors should ever influence any experience.

Dichotomous Reasoning: You believe that everything is "Always, Every, or Never." When someone that you admired makes a mistake, you now have contempt for them.

FAITH G. HARPER, PHD, LPC-S, ACS, ACN is a bad-ass, funny lady with a PhD. She's a licensed professional counselor, board supervisor, certified sexologist, and applied clinical nutritionist with a private practice and consulting business in San Antonio, TX. She has been an adjunct professor and a TEDx presenter, and proudly identifies as a woman of color and uppity intersectional feminist. She is the author of the book *Unf*ck Your Brain* and many other popular zines and books on subjects such as anxiety, depression, and grief. She is available as a public speaker and for corporate and clinical trainings.

"Dr. Faith is a hoot with heart, and her guide is full of workable, professional advice, as well as it is replete with sarcasm, good humor, and grace." —Foreword Reviews

UNF#CK YOUR WORTH

OVERCOME YOUR MONEY EMOTIONS, VALUE YOUR OWN LABOR, AND MANAGE FINANCIAL FREAK-OUTS IN A CAPITALIST HELLSCAPE

FAITH G. HARPER, PHD, LPC-S, ACS, ACN
WALL STREET JOURNAL BESTSELLING AUTHOR OF *UNF#CK YOUR BRAIN*

NEXT, CHECK OUT DR. FAITH'S COMPANION BOOK

Did you enjoy this difficult, deep foray into your internalized views on money? Well, have we got another book for you, *Unfuck Your Worth*!